First Experiences
Jim goes to Hospital

Jim

Jim's Dad

Nurse Jo

Margot Channing

At home

Jim doesn't feel well. His ear aches and he can't hear properly.

He feels a bit dizzy, too.

His sister Betty once had a sore ear, but it got better quickly. Jim's ear is very sore.

Jim's Mum

Betty

Jim

At the surgery

The next day Jim's Mum takes him to see the doctor.

At the surgery, Doctor Smiley looks inside Jim's ear with an otoscope.

He tells Jim that he needs an operation to make it better. Jim will have to go to hospital.

Jim's Mum

Jim

Otoscope

Doctor Smiley

Back home

The postman delivers a letter from the hospital.

The letter tells Jim what day his operation will be and what time he must be in the ward.

Jim's
Mum

Jim

Betty

Getting ready

Jim's Mum packs a bag for him. Jim gets his toothbrush and a comb. He asks Mum to pack his favourite toy, too.

Jim

Jim's Mum

The ward

Jim's Dad takes him to the hospital. The ward has six beds in it.

Nurse Jo will look after him there. She looks very kind and tells Jim's Dad that he can stay, too.

Jim's Dad

Jim

Nurse Jo

All about Jim

Nurse Jo has a laptop. She asks some questions about Jim and about his sore ear.

She writes everything down on her laptop for the doctor to read.

How heavy is Jim?

Nurse Jo takes Jim's temperature with a thermometer. She weighs him to see how heavy he is and listens to his breathing with a stethoscope.

Nurse Jo writes Jim's name on a plastic bracelet and fastens it round his wrist. Now everyone will know who Jim is.

Jim

Weighing machine

Nurse Jo

Preparation

Mr Bone, the surgeon, comes to see Jim and his Dad to tell them what is going to happen.

Nurse Jo helps Jim to put on his theatre gown. It is a special shirt that ties at the back.

Nurse Jo says she has some 'magic' cream to put on Jim's paw to make it feel numb.

Jim

Stethoscope

Nurse Jo

Tube of 'magic' cream

Jim's Dad

Mr Bone

To the theatre

Jim's bed has wheels on it so the porter can wheel him to the operating theatre.

The porter is very cheery and says that his name is Bob. Nurse Jo and Dad come, too.

Nurse Jo

Bob the porter

Jim

Jim's Dad

The operation

Jim has an injection in his paw to make him fall asleep before the operation. Does it hurt? No! Nurse Jo's 'magic' cream has made his paw numb.

Mr Bone smiles and starts to count to ten. One, two, three, four, five... six... Jim is asleep.

Mr Bone

Jim

Recovery

The operation is over. When Jim wakes up he is back on the ward. He has a big, soft bandage over his ear.

Betty is here, too. Mum has gone to buy a comic for Jim.

Jim feels very thirsty, so Nurse Jo brings him something to eat and drink. Soon he can go to the playroom.

Success!

Mr Bone comes to check on Jim's ear. He says the operation has been a great success.

Jim's ear is better now.
He can go home.

Farewell

Mum, Dad and Betty arrive to take Jim home. Mum has a bunch of flowers for Jim to give to Nurse Jo.

Jim thanks her for being so kind and waves goodbye.

Nurse Jo

Jim's Mum

Jim's Dad

Jim

Notes for parents and carers

A hospital stay can be a stressful time for adults and children. Children will worry about being away from home and having to sleep in a strange place. They will probably be anxious about injections and tests that may hurt. Having an operation is a difficult concept for a young child to fully understand, so they are likely to be fearful of what it will entail.

Fortunately, children's wards nowadays are generally bright, friendly places. Parents or carers can stay with their child practically all of the time, day and night. Pain relief is well controlled, and the nursing staff take great care to explain all procedures to each child, to reassure them and allay their fears.

Care should be taken to make sure that small children do not think that going into hospital is a punishment. It may be possible for parents and children to visit the hospital before the operation to introduce its strange smells, sounds and activities. Sometimes teachers will hold discussions in the classroom about the experience of going into hospital, and children can contribute by talking about their own experience. Children in hospital appreciate cards, news and visits from their school friends, and being kept up with school work while they are away.

- Don't prepare the child too far ahead; two or three days is sufficient for a three- to five-year-old.
- Never pretend on the day that the child is going somewhere else.
- Reassure the child that they will not be alone: Mum, Dad or a carer will be with them throughout their stay in hospital.
- Let the child choose one or two favourite things to take with them to hospital as a comfort.
- Once in hospital, make sure that the child knows what is about to happen and why, and whether it will hurt.
- Consult the child and allow them to make small choices about their care. This will help them to feel part of the process.

Some helpful websites:
http://www.netdoctor.co.uk/health_advice/facts/childrenhospital.htm
http://www.bartsandthelondonkids.nhs.uk/

Wordlist

doctor
A doctor finds out what is wrong with you and helps you get better.

hospital
A place people go to when they are sick or injured.

injection
A medicine that makes you fall asleep before an operation.

numb
Not able to feel pain.

nurse
A person who cares for the sick.

operating theatre
A room in a hospital where operations take place.

operation
What a surgeon does to mend something inside your body.

otoscope (or auriscope)
An instrument used by a doctor to look into your ears.

porter
A person who helps in a hospital.

stethoscope
An instrument used by a doctor to listen to the sounds your body makes.

surgeon
A doctor who carries out operations.

temperature
A measure of how hot or cold something is.

thermometer
An instrument used to measure temperature.

ward
A room in a hospital where you are looked after before and after an operation.

Index